the YEAR ROUND Christmas TREE

Written and Illustrated by Kim Wasden

1

"Mommy, why are you getting out the Christmas tree now?" Paige asked, as her mother pulled a large box down from the hot attic.

"It's not Christmas time!"

Her mother gently laid the box on the floor. Then she pulled down an old photo album from a shelf and opened it to a picture of Paige's grandmother.

Summer Tree

Mommy

Grandma + Mommy

"When I was a little girl, my sisters and I would help your grandma decorate our tree throughout the year. We called it the year round Christmas tree. Many of our favorite childhood memories are of my family and me making ornaments and decorating together. It reminded us to celebrate God's love and gifts all year."

Paige thought about that and asked,
"What are we celebrating now?

It's summer!"

Mommy thought, "I am thankful for vacation and time
with my family. I am also thankful for warmer weather
and sunshine. What are some things you enjoy about
summer, Paige?"

6

"The beach!" Paige said excitedly.

I also love riding my bike
and eating ice cream."

"Those are great things to be thankful for in the
summer," Mommy responded.

Then Paige's mom took the craft box with paper, glue, buttons, glitter, and lots of other fun craft supplies from the closet. Paige was so excited to get started! They sat down and made paper suns and foam flip-flops and sunglasses. Paige painted polka dots and flowers on her flip-flop ornaments. She then glued three pink pom-poms together for strawberry ice cream and wrapped a brown piece of felt around the bottom for a cone.

"It looks good enough to eat!"

thought Paige.

After their ornaments dried, Mommy and Paige had a fun time decorating the tree. Paige could not wait to show Daddy when he got home.

Paige had enjoyed working on their first tree.

Now summer vacation was nearing an end. The days were turning cooler and school would start soon.

"Mommy, can we change our summer tree for the fall?" asked Paige.

"Yes, Paige, and what would be good decorations for a fall tree?" Mommy replied.

"Leaves and pumpkins!" suggested Paige.

"We'll remember Thanksgiving and all of God's blessings," Mommy said.

With cold soft clay they made miniature pumpkins. Paige enjoyed the squishy feeling of the clay as she rolled it around in her hands and formed round balls. Then, using a small stick, she pressed in the lines of the pumpkins. They would leave the pumpkins to dry and paint them various shades of orange the next day.

Since Paige still wanted more ornaments, Mommy said, "Let's see what we can find from nature."

They went outside and collected colorful leaves of gold and orange.

When they came back inside Paige said, "I have an idea Mommy. What if we make paper leaves so everyone can take one and write on it what they are thankful for?"

Mommy said, "Thats a terrific idea!"

Paige cut, folded, and glued the leaves out of colored paper.

Mommy helped her place
the colorful creations on
the tree and hang beautiful
ribbon around it.

Soon aunts, uncles, cousins, grandparents, and friends were visiting and
celebrating for the holidays. Paige was thrilled at all the paper leaves with
blessings written on them.

On Thanksgiving Day, they took the leaves off the tree and read them as they gathered around the table. They were amazed by the number of paper leaves that covered the table. Paige was very thankful for all of God's blessings.

Now Thanksgiving had come and gone and soon there was snow on the lawn. "I know what we are celebrating now, Mommy. God's greatest gift...Jesus!", Paige exclaimed as she helped Mommy bring down the boxes of Christmas ornaments and decorations.

Mommy turned on the Christmas music and made hot chocolate as Paige and Daddy began decorating.

On Christmas Eve, the family sat down to read the Christmas story. Paige gazed at the little nativity on the mantle as Daddy began to read from the Bible.

"God sent his own Son to be born in a manger for us," Paige thought. "He must really love us a lot."

Paige was always a little sad to take down the tree after Christmas. This year however, she was excited to see how they would decorate for a winter tree.

For winter, Paige and Mommy decided to design a blue, white, and silver tree to celebrate the beauty of God's creation. They wanted the tree to reflect the snow and icicles that were outside.

Paige and her mom covered the tree with blue ribbon along with blue and silver ornaments. They twisted together icicles and snowflakes out of tinsel pipe cleaners. They also made snowflakes by gluing popsicle sticks together, painting them white and sprinkling glitter on them.

Soon it seemed that Paige was covered head to toe with glitter.

"It makes you sparkle like the tree!"
Mommy laughed.

After all the fun decorating, Paige bundled up and
went outside to play in the snow.

Before long it was February, and Paige and Mommy decided to turn the tree into a Valentines tree.

Mommy asked Paige, "Do you know what Jesus said was the greatest commandment?"

Paige answered excitedly, "I learned that in church!"

"Love the Lord with all your **heart.** *"*

Mommy responded, "Very good, Paige. Do you know the second part of that commandment?"

"What is it Mommy?" Paige asked

"Love you neighbor as yourself." Mommy answered.

"Valentine's Day
    is a good reminder about how to treat
    others by sharing

God's love."

The two of them cut out red, pink, and purple paper hearts and decorated them with sequins and heart stickers. Paige decorated one of them especially for her dad and put it aside to give to him when he got home. It was laced with ribbon and had a big "I LOVE YOU!" in the middle.

Spring arrived, and the weather began to turn warmer. Paige enjoyed watching the trees come to life again with green leaves. The flowers were beginning to bloom, and a bird built a nest on the tree outside her windowsill.

One day Paige noticed three little blue eggs in the nest! Paige watched the eggs in the nest every day and waited for one to hatch.

"We have almost completed our first year round Christmas tree!" Mommy told Paige.

"What celebration do you think comes next?"

Paige thought, and then smiled wide. "Easter!" We'll decorate an Easter tree!" said Paige.

He is Risen!

"That's right Paige," Mommy responded. "God sent Jesus to die for our sins. He rose on Easter so we can live in heaven with Him. Easter is a celebration of new life. And just as there is new life each spring happening all around us outside, God offers us new life forever through Jesus."

For **God** so *loved* the world,

    that he gave his only begotten Son,

       that whosoever believeth in him should not perish,

but have *everlasting life.*

                John 3:16

They decided to decorate the tree with Easter eggs, small crosses, flowers, and tiny bird's nests. They made the eggs out of clay and painted them. To make flowers, they cut out shapes from colorful felt and added buttons and beads.

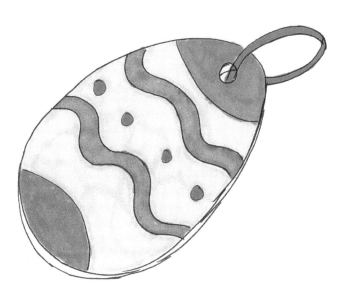

Paige had the most fun making crosses. She glued pieces of bright tissue paper to wax paper, and after it dried she cut out the shape of a cross. It looked like a stain glass window.

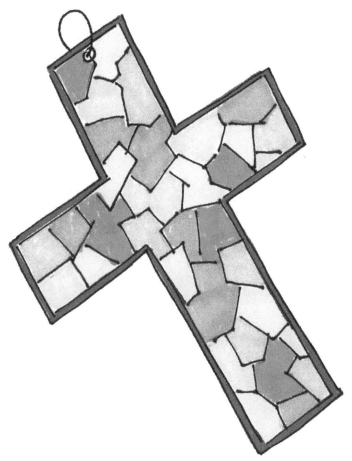

"This is so much fun, Mommy!", exclaimed Paige.

"I love making our own ornaments."

33

Later that day, Paige looked out her window at the bird's nest.

"Mommy, Daddy! Come Look!" she exclaimed.

They all crowded around and watched as three tiny beaks poked out of the nest with their mouths wide open.

"What a great reminder of new life and God's love." Daddy said.

Paige looked up at her mom and dad and
at the tree they had worked on all year.

"Thank You, God, for Your blessings this year!

Help us always be thankful for Your Son, our Savior." Paige prayed.

Now it is your turn to create your own Year Round Christmas Tree. It is my hope and prayer that you can begin your own tradition as a family. May your Year Round Christmas Tree be a reminder to your family of God's many blessings year round. To help you I have included the instructions, recipes, and templates for your use. Have fun and be creative!

Supplies:

This is a general list of supplies that will be used throughout projects. Often there are multiple ways to make many of the ornaments. Choose the option that works best for you and the supplies that you have on hand. The templates and recipes will follow the instruction section.

- Scissors
- Glue (basic white craft glue and or felt glue)
- Hot glue gun and glue sticks
- Acrylic craft paint, brushes
- Colored felt sheets and or colored foam sheets
- Pony beads, buttons, self-adhesive rhinestones, stickers
- Pipe cleaners, Popsicle sticks, Styrofoam balls
- Colored pom poms of various sizes
- Ribbon, yarn, needles
- Colored and decorative paper scraps, tissue paper
- Wax paper, Contact Paper
- Shrinky Dink
- Hole punch
- Flour, salt, cinnamon, applesauce, or air dry clay
- Various other materials from around the house and outside including but not limited to: pine cones, leaves, fabric scraps, seashells, cardboard, puzzle pieces, cotton balls, wood scraps, shaped pasta, soft wire, candy hearts, etc.

☀ Summer Tree ☀

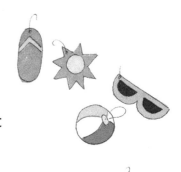

Flip Flops, Sunshines, Sunglasses, and Beach Balls

Cut out the ornament shapes from pieces of craft foam, felt, or paper. The templates are in the back of the book. Cut out details from a contrasting color and glue onto your shape with white craft glue. All of these shapes could also be cut out of salt dough, baked, and painted with craft paint.

Styrofoam Sunshine

Paint small styrofoam balls with yellow craft paint. Cut pipe cleaners of yellow, orange, and gold to a desire length and carefully poke each into the ball. Leave one a little longer to bend over as a hook.

Felt Flowers

Trace and cut out flower shapes from various colors of felt. Use fabric glue to layer center pieces and smaller petals on top of each other. Glue or sew beads or buttons to add decoration.

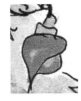

Sea Shell Ornaments

Hot glue ribbon to the back of sea shells. Leave them their natural colors or paint them with acrylic paint.

Pom Pom Ice Cream Ornaments

Cut a small triangle out of brown construction paper or foam. Bend two sides up towards each other overlapping to form a cone. Glue in place. Join three colored pom poms together gluing with hot glue or craft glue. Glue a red button or pony bead on the top for a cherry.

Surfboards

Cut surfboard shapes out of thin cardboard (cereal boxes), foam, or cardstock. If using cardboard or cardstock, paint designs with craft paint and add glitter or decorative paper for designs. If using foam, glue contrasting color foam shapes for designs.

Popsicles

Cut out the popsicle shape from craft cardstock or thin cardboard. Paint bright solid colors or strips for a rainbow popsicle. Glue a popsicle stick to the back and attach a string through the top to hang.

Colorful Fish

Use the beach ball circle template for the body of the fish. Cut out of craft paper or foam. Cut out the fins and tail from different colors and glue the edges to the back side of the body. Add contrasting colors by cutting and gluing designs from paper or use markers or paint to decorate.

Felt or Paper Leaves

Cut out leaf shapes from decorative paper, cardstock, felt, or foam. Could also cut out of cinnamon dough. Follow recipe in the back.

Mini Pumpkins

Rounded pumpkins: Use salt dough or air dry clay. Take a tablespoon of clay and form it into a ball. Using a toothpick or small stick press the lines of the pumpkins into the clay. Pinch a little of the clay from the top to form the stem and poke a small hole in the stem using a toothpick.

Flat pumpkins: Roll out the dough or clay to 1/4 inch think. Trace a pumpkin shape stencil with a kitchen knife or use a cookie cutter to cut the shapes. Follow the drying or baking instructions and then paint with craft paint.

Acorns, Pinecones, and Leaves

Collect these from outside to use on your tree. You can spray paint, paint with craft paint, or leave natural.

Sunflowers

Trace and cut the flower shape out of yellow and orange felt or paper. Glue or sew a brown button in the middle.

Felt Turkey

Using the turkey template cut the pieces from felt. Join together using felt glue. Glue or sew buttons or beads for eyes.

 Christmas Tree

Felt Baby Jesus

Use the template and cut the three shapes out of felt. Use felt glue to glue them together. Use thread and needle to blanket stitch around the edge of the blue felt. (Optional)

Popsicle Nativity

Use three wide popsicle sticks. Paint the tops a skin color. Use scraps of cloth or ribbon to glue on as clothing. Use a black sharpie to draw the faces on.

Pom Pom Wreath

Hot glue red and green pom poms in a circle. Use ribbon or yarn to tie and hang.

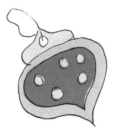

Decorative Paper Ornaments

Use assorted Christmas scrapbook and cardstock paper. Trace and cut ornament shapes. Layer smaller shapes on top and glue in place. Decorate with sequins or glitter. Hole punch at the top and use yarn or ribbon to attach.

Yarn Trees

Use the triangle tree template. Cut those shapes from thin cardboard. Using yarn, glue one end of the yarn to the cardboard. Start at any point and begin wrapping the shape with the yarn. Change directions and keep working the yarn all over the shape till the whole shape is covered.

Felt Holly

Use the holly template and trace onto green felt. Cut it out. Glue three to four red beads onto the felt for berries.

Salt Dough Stars and Stockings

Use the salt dough recipe in the back. Roll out a slab 1/4 inch thick. Use template shapes or cookie cutters to cut out shapes.

❄ Winter Tree ❄

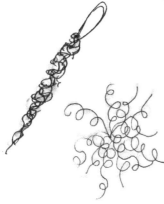

Icicles and Sparkle Stars

Twist together silver and white pipe cleaners and use a pencil to spiral bend them around the pencil to look like icicles. Sparkle star - take 4 silver, white, or blue pipe cleaners, bunch 3 together wrapping the fourth around the middle to secure. Take each section, spread them apart, twist, and curl it.

Puzzle Piece Snowflake

Paint old puzzle pieces white with acrylic craft paint. When dry, glue together in the shape of a snowflake. Hot glue ribbon or yarn to hang.

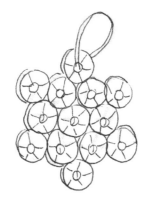

Pasta Wagon Wheel Snowflake

Draw out a simple line design of a snowflake on wax paper. Carefully arrange your pasta pieces down on the wax paper and glue together. Use school glue and allow to dry for a couple of hours. Once glue is dry spray paint or paint with acrylic white or silver paint. While the paint is still wet, sprinkle with glitter.

Popsicle Stick Snowflake

Take four popsicle sticks and paint them white. After they dry take two at a time and hot glue together in an X. Glue those two X's together to form a snowflake shape. Brush a thin layer of watered down glue or modge podge over the snowflake and sprinkle glitter over the snowflake.

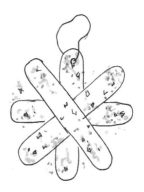

Felt Mittens

Use the mitten template and cut out mitten shapes from felt or craft foam. Glue or sew on buttons, beads, and yarn designs.

Salt Dough Snowman Face

Roll the dough out and cut out a 2 inch circle for the snowman's face. Mold a carrot shape out of the dough for the nose and attach. Add a hat shape to the top of his head. Bake according to directions, cool, and then paint.

Wood Round Snowman

Use precut wood rounds. Draw a half circle on the bottom half and paint white. Paint the background black with white dots for snow flakes. The snowman is looking up catching the snowflakes. Paint his nose orange and give him black dots of coal for his mouth. Hot glue a ribbon on the back to hang.

Mini Stars

Trace and cut from felt, paper, or craft foam. These can also be made from salt dough, clay, or cinnamon dough.

♡ Valentines Tree ♡

Paper Hearts

Cut heart shapes out of decorative cardstock paper. Keep as solid heart shapes or fold and cut a smaller heart from the center. You can also string multiple hearts together like the example.

Candied Heart

Cut heart shape out of thin cardboard. Using candy hearts with messages on them, glue a series of them together to outline the shape of the heart. Glue a string or ribbon to the top for hanging.

Pipe Cleaner Heart Chain

Use red, pink, and white pipe cleaners. Bend one into a heart shape, twisting the ends together. Loop a second one into the first and bend it into a heart. Continue to do the same to create a chain of hearts. They can also be made and hung as individual shapes.

Salt Dough Hearts

Roll the dough out 1/4 inch thick. Use cookie cutters or templates to cut out heart shapes. Bake according to directions, cool, and paint.

Yarn Heart

Use the heart template and cut a heart from thin cardboard. Using yarn, glue one end of the yarn to the cardboard. Start at any point and begin wrapping the shape with the yarn. Change directions and keep working the yarn all over the shape till the whole shape is covered.

❀Spring/Easter Tree❀

Mod Podge Egg

Cut out a cardboard egg. Tear little pieces of decorative paper and or tissue paper. Spread a thin layer of mod podge over the egg with an old paint brush and layer the torn paper on the egg spreading a thin layer of glue on top to seal the paper. Add glitter to the modge podge (optional). This technique can also be done with other shapes.

Tissue Paper Stain Glass

Use the contact paper instructions in the recipe section. Cut out your egg and cross shape boarders and using small pieces of tissue paper cover the sticky side of the contact paper. Don't forget to add the other layer of contact paper.

Paper Flowers / Bunny Garland

Use templates and cut out shapes from decorative paper. Use a hole punch to punch holes and string shapes together. These can be longer ornaments or garland.

Toilet Paper Roll Ornaments

Chick - Carefully cut a toilet paper roll down to 2 inches. Paint yellow. Cut and add yellow pipe cleaners for wings, feet, and hair. Use sharpies to draw the face.

Bird House - Cut the roll to 3 inches, slanting the top. Paint. Cut a 2x6 inch rectangle from cardstock. Fold in half and glue on top for roof. Decorate with paint or sharpies.

Salt Dough or Clay Bunnies, Lambs, Eggs, and Birds

Roll the dough out 1/4 inch thick. Use cookie cutters or templates to cut out fun shapes. Bake according to directions, cool, and paint.

Egg Wreath

Cut out a circle ring from cardboard. Cut small egg shapes from decorative paper and glue them onto the cardboard circle. Add glitter, buttons, and or beads as desired.

Shrinky Dink (Carrots, Eggs, Butterflys, crosses, chicks, etc.)

Use template shapes to trace shapes onto the sheets of shrinky dink. Use permanent markers to color the shapes in. Cut the shapes out. Follow the directions on the packet to bake and shrink the shapes

Twirling Folded Egg

Cut 4 identical egg shapes from various decorative pieces of paper. Fold the eggs in half lengthwise. Take one of the folded pieces. Apply a thin layer of glue to one side. Lay another folded egg over the glued side matching the edges. Do the same to the remaining to eggs. Cut a piece of yarn three times the length of one egg. Fold it in half and lay in the center of one side of egg leaving a loop at the top and yarn at the bottom. Glue the other half of the egg over the yarn joining the two halves together. Knot a bead at the top and the bottom on the yarn.

 Recipes

Salt Dough Recipe

1/2 cup of salt

1/2 cup of water

1 cup of flour

Instructions: Salt Dough

Mix 1/2 cup of salt and 1 cup of flour together and stir in the water adding it slowly. You may not need all of the water. If the dough gets sticky add more flour. Knead the dough and then roll out and use as needed. Use cookie cutters or drawn patterns. You can also mold and shape your ornaments to be more dimensional. Next bake your shapes at 200 for 3 hours. Let them cool and then paint with acrylic craft paint.

Mod Podge Recipe

1 cup white glue

1/3 cut of water

Mix together and use an old paint brush to apply. Add fine glitter to the mixture to add shine to your project.

Cinnamon Dough

Materials:

1/2 cup applesauce

3/4 cup ground cinnamon

3 Tbsp white school glue,

Extra cinnamon

Instructions:Cinnamon Dough

Combine glue and ground cinnamon in a bowl. Add applesauce, stirring constantly until you have a stiff dough. Remove dough onto the table and knead for 5 minutes until firm. Let rest 30 minutes at room temperature. Roll dough out on waxed paper to about 1/8 inch thick. Cut out with cookie cutters of your choice. Poke a hole in the top with a straw. Leave for 48 hours to one week in a warm breezy area. Turn over every 24 hours to help them dry evenly.

Contact Paper Ornaments

Fold a piece of construction paper in half and cut out a shape. About an inch from the edge of that shape, cut a smaller identical shape from the middle. You will be left with an inch wide boarder of the shape with empty space in the middle. Cut a square of clear contact paper that is a little larger than your shape. Place it sticky side up and place your shape on top. Next cut small pieces of tissue paper. Lay them down in the middle of your shape, filling up the empty space on the contact paper. Cut another square of contact paper and place it on top sandwiching your shape with the tissue paper in the middle. Trim around the edge leaving a small edge of contact paper around the shape to keep it sealed. Punch a hole in the top and hang with ribbon or yarn.

Wax Paper and Crayon Meltings

With an adults help carefully shave pieces of crayon into little bits using a kitchen knife or X-acto knife. Make sure to shave away from yourself. Fold a piece of wax paper or paper in half. Open it and sprinkle the crayon shavings on one half. Fold and place a piece of paper or a thin towel over it. On low heat setting, use an iron to melt the crayon. When it cools you can cut the wax paper or paper into ornament shapes. Hearts, Easter eggs, butterflys, crosses, etc. Use a hole punch and yarn to finish.

Transparent Paper

Color an image with crayons on white copy paper. Use crayons, NOT markers or colored pencils. Use a small amount of cooking oil and cotton balls. Turn your paper on the backside and rub a small amount of oil on the back. You'll see the paper turn transparent and the colors come through. Put them aside to dry. You can frame the shape with construction paper or punch a hole and hang as is.

Shrinky Dink Instructions

Buy Shrinky Dink sheets at crafts stores. Trace the shape you want and color with permanent markers. Punch a hole at the top of your shape. Lay on top of parchment paper on a sheet pan and bake for 3 min at 325. This material can be used for a number of ornament ideas for all seasons. The kids love to watch it shrink.

← Circle can also be used for snowman head and fish body

Fish tail

top fin

Surfboard

Bottom fins

Popsicle

Summer

Fall

Turkey Head

Turkey
tail feathers
(cut 6)

Christmas

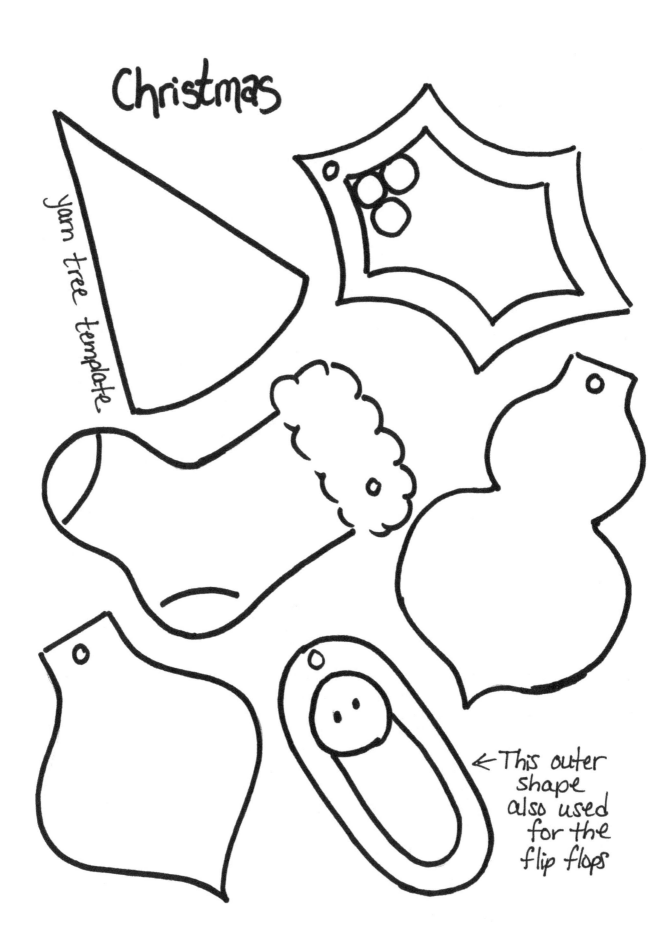

yarn tree template

←This outer shape also used for the flip flops

Winter +
Valentines

Spring   Easter

About the Story

On a long twelve hour drive to New York a couple of years ago, I was trying to entertain my girls in the car. I began to write out stories to read to them and this story emerged as I took ideas we had done as a family and added fictional characters. I began to draw illustrations to go with the story, and my family encouraged me to complete and publish it. It became a dream that I believe God gave me, and although it has taken years, the dream never left.

The most important message is the one of salvation, woven into the story and it is a message we should remember all year. I believe God wants us to share this story! As you decorate the tree, let it be a conversation starter to share God's love with others. I pray you will slow down as a family, take time to do the crafts together, and remember all that God has done for you.

Kim Wasden

For Fun Throughout the book Paige has her puppy beside her. Sometimes she is partly hidden. See how many puppies you can find.

Other Tree Ideas Add other celebrations to your tree. They do not all have to be holidays. Maybe there is something that is special to your family that would make a great theme for a tree. A few ideas are: 4th of July Tree, Birthday Tree, Princess Tree, Back to School Tree, and Travel Tree! *Be Creative!*

the YEr urand Tree!

Contact :

f *Paintwithpraise*

O *paint_with_praise*

www.paintwithpraise.com

paintwithpraise@gmail.com

Share your creative ideas. Send me pictures of your ornaments and trees.

Drawn by my daughter Faith when I first started the book. She was 5 years old.

CPSIA information can be obtained
at www.ICGtesting.com
Printed in the USA
LVHW071745231120
672484LV00073B/2081